JUST CALL ME PASTOR

Just Call Me Pastor

A *Peter Pulpitpounder* Book

BY ROBERT E. SEGERHAMMAR

Illustrated by
DONALD J. WALLERSTEDT

AUGUSTANA PRESS
ROCK ISLAND, ILLINOIS

JUST CALL ME PASTOR

TO MY WIFE

JAN

The queen of our parsonage

Introduction

"WRITE ME a story, daddy."

Such was the request of the writer's young daughter as she lay in bed for many months with rheumatic fever.

The result of this request was a series of chapters on the life of a rural minister, later published under the title, "Peter Pulpitpounder, B.D."

Because this book was well received by the reading public, another volume has been attempted at the urging of both children and adults, who have asked that a series of Peter Pulpitpounder books be written. Whether or not a series of such books will be forthcoming is yet to be seen, but following is a second volume at least, giving some account of the life of a city pastor.

No contrast is intended between the relative merits or importance of a rural or a city ministry. Both are equally significant in the religious life of a nation, and we ought to overcome the idea (if it still exists) that a pastor takes a step upward, if he moves from a rural to a city parish.

As a pastor who himself has served both rural and city parishes, I can only say that each has its own characteristics and its own distinctive importance to society. I might also add that I have found that a city pastor is no busier than a rural minister; they are both as busy as they allow themselves to be, but each being busier than the other with certain phases of the work.

This book is, therefore, submitted simply as a description of the life of a minister in just another corner of God's vast pastureland.

R. E. S.

Contents

9

Chapter 1

The Bustling City

ONCE, IN A BIG BUSTLING CITY, there lived a big
bustling man with his big bustling family. He had just
moved away from a happy little village where he had
found great fame as a pulpit-pounding preacher; for
this mighty man of God learned to pound his pulpit
with such skill that people sat straight up and took
notice when he preached to them.

This famous preacher had no choice but to pound
his fist when he delivered his sermons, for he had lost

his shaking finger years before in a quarrel with a power saw, and since he could no longer shake his accusing finger at his listeners, he had to pound his pulpit to punctuate his sentences. And so, although he was basically a quiet man, his reputation changed from a peaceful preacher to a thunderous pulpitpounder, all because he decided to live up to his name.

The people of the little village had loved this unusual man. Indeed, it had become a village saying (after he moved away) that never was this tiny town blessed with a more unusual pastor, for he was the quiet and the quaint, the common and the colorful, the kind and the clever, all wrapped up in one big round package and tied together with bands of love.

But now this reverend minister had left the quiet little village. He had accepted an invitation to move to the big bustling city with its pounding wheels of street and factory, its noisy clatter, and its rushing masses. For the fame of his pulpit pounding had spread both far and wide, and this big church in this big city thought no one could better fill their pulpit than this round, round man, and few preachers could pound home a message quite so well in this noisy, pounding city as the Rev. Dr. Peter Paul Pulpitpounder, A.B., B.D., D.D.

And so the day for fond farewells had come to the little village. Peter had sold some of his furniture and packed the rest. The boxes of books from his library were stacked, like mountains, in the empty office, and some of the tender keepsakes that Peter and his wife had kept since the day of their marriage were lovingly laid in cardboard cartons and sealed for the day of happy reopening. The records of the church (the baptisms, the communions, the funerals) and all the other lists of church members and their activities were carefully checked, like a house being put in order. The water was shut off, the switch in the fuse box was pulled, the telephone was disconnected, and another chapter in the life of the Pulpitpounders had come to an end. It was a sad day both for the pastor's family and the people of the little church; but so it is in the life of pulpit pounders and their parishes. But still, the tears shed by young and old were not bitter tears, for they all knew that some day they would be together again in the place where no moving vans are ever allowed, and where no fuse boxes are ever found, because in this place they never turn off the lights.

Of course, the tears of sadness in leaving the village church were soon replaced by tears of joy in the church of the bustling city. No sooner had the moving van backed its heavy door to the porch of the parsonage than a dozen men from the congregation were swarming around the house, helping to unload the boxes from the van and the pulpitpounderettes from the pastor's car.

And when the pastor's wife walked into her new home for the first time, she found a dozen women giving the house its last minute touches with the mop and the dust cloth, curiously opening boxes of dishes and stacking them on the newly papered shelves. Mrs. Pulpitpounder found no difficulty in feeling at home in her new kitchen, for when she opened the new refrigerator which the congregation had just bought, she discovered it was filled with eggs and milk, fruit and vegetables, and even some of Mrs. Hanson's home-canned peach sauce and Mrs. Olson's home-made jellies.

All was gaiety and excitement in the parsonage until suddenly the phone rang in the empty house, and its echo startled everyone. Trustee Peterson lifted the receiver. It was the Carlson family calling for the minister. Mr. Carlson was deathly sick, and wanted his new pastor to give him Holy Communion before he left for the heavenly kingdom.

Quickly Peter ripped open his boxes until he found his communion vessels, and then, taking these and his Bible, he set out to find the stricken home in the bustling city, bringing these saddened people the comfort of the heavenly Father. Peter was tired from the long drive to the big city, and nothing would have

14

pleased him more than a few moments of quiet rest, and perhaps a tasty cup of afternoon coffee. But Peter always put duty before pleasure, and longed to be useful to his church and his Lord. So, taking time only to wash his hands and say a prayer, the pastor went out on this first mission of service and love, knowing that no deed of kindness and no stroke of helpfulness is ever without its blessings to the people of earth and its joy to the angels of heaven.

And so began the busy life of Dr. Peter Paul Pulpitpounder in the big bustling city—a life of love and busy service which began for this dedicated man even before he could unpack his bags.

Chapter 2

The New Parsonage

WHEN PETER PULPITPOUNDER returned from the
Carlson home in his Ford, which was still loaded with
suitcases and boxes, he found that the helpers from the
congregation had all gone home. The moving van had
left, and the Pulpitpounders were alone in their new
home for the first time.

A strange feeling came over Peter as he saw his old
familiar furniture standing by those unfamiliar walls

and windows. He knew these rooms had seen much living—fun and excitement, but also sorrow—in the years gone by. These walls had heard little prayers of simple trust ascend to heaven from the lips of children just learning to talk, and they had heard big prayers of deep concern from the lips of pastors who had talked long and fervently with God about problems that faced them and their parishioners. The ceilings had nearly been raised by families who stood around the piano and sang hymns of praise to the Lord of heaven; and the windows had let in much light and fresh air over the years, especially after illness had besieged the home, and long and trying times of sickness had visited the families that had lived in this house in the days now past. Behind the desk in the study had sat many a devoted minister, and one loyal pastor's wife after another had scrubbed these floors and washed dishes in this sink. And behind the house was a path that led to a tiny shed, and through the rafters of this old barn had come the cries of preachers' boys who were learning the price of naughtiness or of making too much noise.

Yes, much living had gone into this house, and, as Peter looked at these strange rooms, an awesome feeling came over him. He and his family were entering into the labors of others, and now they were adding the next chapter to the living that had taken place in this parsonage. It made Peter feel that he was not alone in his new house, and soon he began to feel at home—and happy.

But then Peter noticed the wallpaper! A cold chill went down his back as he thought of the rugs which

17

were as yet unrolled, for he just knew his rugs and this wallpaper would never in a million years look as if they belonged together. And then, as he counted the rooms, he found that this house had seventeen more windows than the parsonage in the little village, and he noticed that most of the others were different in size and shape from the curtains the Pulpitpounders brought with them. Peter and his wife wondered what they would do about these and many other problems that faced them.

But before they had a chance to think about the answer to these questions they were startled by the sound of loud voices that came from the bedrooms upstairs.

Hurrying up the steps to the room where most of the noise seemed to be, Peter found Carol, Helen and Nancy, Luke and II Peter all demanding the same bedroom. Each had his own reason for claiming this bedroom for himself, although there were plenty of bedrooms to go around in this big house. In fact, the house was so big, it was sometimes jokingly spoken of by the church members as "the hotel," and the congregation had given serious thought to making it into a Sunday school building.

Peter did not have enough furniture to fill this huge house, and what he did have was neither the nicest nor the newest; and yet he thought how different it was now to have so many children and so much furniture when on the day he moved into his first parsonage, all he had was a bride, a school debt, a broken-down typewriter, and a thousand books. But Peter never envied those who had more or better things than he, for he believed that "godliness with contentment is great gain," and he often quoted the apostle who said, "I have learned, in whatever state I am, to be content." And Peter had learned not to worry or fret over the things he did not have, because life had taught him that God always supplies us with what we need, if we simply trust His fatherly goodness.

Now before the little matter of bedroom assignments could be settled (which for so large a family was like settling the twelve tribes of Israel in the Promised Land), Matthew came running in with a bleeding finger. He had tried to open one of the boxes and had cut his finger on the string, and now the wild rush to find the box with the medicine chest was

19

started. One carton after another was opened, until finally the medicine box was found. Peter painted Matthew's finger with "creatone" as Nancy called the Mercurochrome, and then wrapped the finger with a bandaid (the favorite treatment for all cuts and bruises among children—even the smallest—for more things are done by bandaids than this world dreams of, especially for boys and girls).

And while he looked at the tiny cut on his son's finger, Peter mused, "Maybe Matthew will grow up to be a pulpitpounder like his father—especially if he isn't more careful with his fingers."

Chapter 3

Peter Tries the Freeway

BEFORE PETER PULPITPOUNDER was through un-
packing his boxes, and long before he had all of his
furniture and pictures in their places, he discovered
that he needed more curtain rods for the upstairs windows. After scratching his balding head with his stubby
finger, he announced to his family, "I shall brave the
treachery of city traffic and drive to a hardware store
for some curtain rods."

As Peter walked out of the house, he heard little
feet following him. He paused briefly, and then cau-

tiously turned his head to see if what he feared might indeed be true. His guess was right—all seven children were following him to the car like little mice following the Pied Piper. Protests and logical arguments were fruitless, and before Peter could say "pax vobiscum," the children were in the car, and already demanding that he buy them some bubble gum.

As Peter backed the car out of the driveway, his wife called from the front porch, "Would you mind stopping at the grocery store for a few things, dear?" Long experience had taught this patient man that such a request could mean anything from picking up a loaf of bread to buying the week's supply of pantry goods on bargain day. But Peter was an understanding man, and he knew how much it meant to his good wife to have the children off her hands and out from under her feet for even a little while; and sending them on a shopping expedition would let her freedom last a little longer.

With the grocery list safely tucked in his black appointment book, Peter set out to find a shopping center with a hardware store and a supermarket. Now what little Peter knew about big city traffic could have been hid in his short, stubby finger, and before he had made many turns and crossed many intersections, he found himself in serious difficulty.

"What do the arrows stand for, daddy?" inquired Helen Margaret.

"Arrows? What arrows? Oh my, my," Peter exclaimed, wiping his brow with the cuff of his shirt, "I'm going the wrong way on a one-way street. I'm traveling the way that leads to jail! What will I do?

22

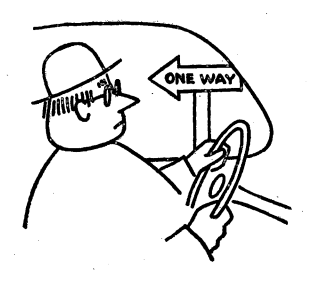

I must turn around." And then he added, his eyes twinkling like stars, "We must be converted and go in the other direction, as I tell my people from the pulpit." And then Peter laughed his "embarrassed laugh" as the children all sang in a chorus, "Oh daddy, oh daddy, you're funny!"

No sooner did the Rev. Dr. Peter Pulpitpounder turn his car around and start in the right direction than he found himself in the thick of heavy traffic. All went well until he had to stop—because all the cars around him were stopping. Inch by inch they seemed to creep toward the corner and the children wondered why they were going so slowly.

Mark pushed his head through the open window, and looking out over the great mass of automobiles, he saw that the stop light on the corner was red. Soon it turned green, and all the cars began to honk and move forward slowly again. But before the cars had moved very far, they all stopped again for the light had already turned red.

As they waited for the light to change again, Carol asked, "What time is it, daddy?"

Peter glanced at his watch. It was five o'clock. This was the rush hour on the city streets. All the workers were going home at the same time, and the swarms of automobiles looked like an army of ants crawling around an ant hill. Just then the light turned green again, and the Pulpitpounder car crept ahead a few more feet. When the streams of cars came to a halt once more, Peter's blood pressure began to rise, especially when from the back seat came the little voice of Nancy Elizabeth. "Daddy," she declared, "I wanna' dink. I wanna' dink."

"Oh no," thought Peter, "not now. We're in the middle of a traffic jam and the gas station is clear across the intersection."

But three more light changes, and four more requests later, and the Pulpitpounder car was across the intersection and free to go wherever the driver pleased. Peter pulled into the filling station, and when all the children's little needs were cared for and the windows were washed and dried, they were on their way again, still in search of the shopping center.

As Peter endeavored to follow the instructions of the station attendant, he started in the right direction. "Did he say to turn a sharp right or a wide right at this corner?" he asked Luke, his oldest son, who was a medical student. The swift traffic left him with little

24

time to ponder the question, and suddenly Peter had made a sharp right turn. To his amazement, he found himself driving on the freeway.

Now Peter had heard of freeways but never, never had he driven on one, and as he sped along, bumper to bumper with the other cars, it seemed ever so simple, especially since all four rows of cars were going in the same direction and there were no stop signs to obey.

Down the super highway they sped, until suddenly Peter realized that he was going somewhere in a tremendous hurry. The only problem was that he did not know where he was going. "I know I must turn left along here somewhere," he told the keys as they dangled on the dashboard. But then Peter realized suddenly that he could not make a left turn on a freeway because then he would run into four lanes of cars speeding in the other direction. "Heavens," exclaimed Peter, "how do you get off this thing? I'll drive half way across the city before I'll figure out how to turn left on the freeway."

Peter decided to work toward the right lane of traffic and stop so he could look at the city map. As he was slowing down ever so carefully, he heard what he thought was an ambulance racing down the road. But just as he thought the ambulance would pass him, it became clear to Peter that he was being run down by a policeman on a motorcycle.

As the officer stepped up to Peter's parked car, the children got quiet as little church mice, something his children did so seldom that Peter almost thanked the policeman for stopping him.

25

"Ya violated Code 247, mister," barked the patrolman.

"I what?" inquired Peter.

"Ya violated the code. Yer drivin' too slow on the freeway."

Peter had preached the gospel for so many years, he knew it was useless to argue with the law. "Well," thought Peter, "I'd be glad to pay a fine just to get off this merry-go-round. I feel like I've been on a rollercoaster ever since I turned right at the corner ten miles back."

Peter tucked the court summons in his appointment book, along with the grocery list, and thanked the officer for instructing him how to turn right and then go under the freeway to make a left turn. As Peter spun around the cloverleaf and started back toward the shopping center, he said to his children, "I guess this will teach me not to start driving in the big city without knowing where I'm going."

And then, as the car pulled up to the shopping center, all the Pulpitpounder children sang together like a choral response, "It's closed. It's closed. The shopping center's closed!"

But before our friend had lived in the big city many months, he was driving around on the freeways and pounding the stop and go pedals of his car with the best of them. He even learned to like city driving, because he thought of the traffic as a puzzle to be solved. And Peter was good at solving puzzles, as any man must be who has a wife and seven children to support.

26

Chapter 4

The First Sunday

BY THE END OF THE WEEK, the Pulpitpounders had
found a place for most of their furniture and books,
files and typewriters, dishes, pots and pans which they
brought with them from the tiny village. Little need
did they have for the dishes the first week, however,
for this happy family was invited out to homes in the
congregation for almost every meal, and by Saturday
night, they were so full of food and frolic, they decided to eat a bowl of soup and go early to bed.

It could hardly be said, with so many Saturday night
baths to engineer and half as many heads of hair to
put up in pin curls, that Mrs. Pulpitpounder got to
bed early, but it was still long before midnight when
she crept quietly to her bedroom, and slipped between
the covers to say her evening prayers.

Before she could fall asleep, however, the queen of
the parsonage was summoned from her warm bed by
the commands of the princess of the parsonage, who
was letting the household know from her throne in
the nursery that she wanted a little more love and attention before she would drop off to slumberland. As
Mrs. Pulpitpounder rocked her youngest child, she sang
softly:

27

Go to sleep, my little girl,
With your golden top a-twirl;
You're as precious as a pearl
With each careless little curl.

Go to sleep now, little toes,
Little ears and little nose,
Little eyes about to close
As to sleep my baby goes.

Go to sleep, each little hand,
To the far-off slumberland,
Where the Sandman digs his sand
With his clever fairy band.

Go to sleep, sweet little tummy,
Filled so full, and round and yummy;
Little mouth with crackers crumby,
Go to sleep now for your mummie!

By the time this drowsy mother sang the last verse
of her lullaby, her little child was fast asleep, and
when morning came, all of the Pulpitpounders had
had a good night of peaceful slumber, and were rested
and ready for their first Sunday at the new church in
the big bustling city—all, that is, except Peter. For the
pastor had spent the night tossing and twisting, and
(worst of all) dreaming his Saturday night preacher's
dream. For years Peter had suffered peculiar dreams on
the night before he preached, and these dreams always
had something to do with preaching.

Usually Peter dreamed that the congregation was
singing the last verse of the opening hymn while he
was frantically trying to button his robe from top to

bottom. Just as the congregation would sing "Amen," and he was scheduled to appear before the altar, he would notice his robe had been buttoned wrong, and would have to rip it open and start buttoning it all over again.

And sometimes he dreamed that he could not get his collar buttoned in the back—a special problem for Peter, because his pointing finger, which was missing, was also his buttoning finger; and the harder he tried to use his other fingers, the clumsier he seemed to be. As the end of the hymn came closer and closer, the stubborn collar made him more and more frantic, and when Peter awoke on Sunday mornings, he was usually exhausted from such agonizing dreams and visions.

Small wonder it was, then, that Peter should have a Saturday night preacher's dream on the eve of his first Sunday with his new congregation. For some strange reason, however, his dream on this important night was not about buttoning robes or collars at all. Nor was it about the opening hymn of the service. Instead Peter dreamed that he was in the pulpit of his new church, and was about to preach his initial sermon. But when he looked out over the congregation and took a deep breath, placed his hands firmly on the pulpit rail (which felt as different from the pulpit in the tiny village as a new shoe) and said reverently, "Let us pray," he noticed to his great amazement that the pulpit was facing the wrong direction. Instead of looking out over the front of the pulpit, he was looking out over the back steps.

And then, to Peter's great embarrassment, he dreamed that he was not wearing his robe, but instead was

vested in a pair of "bib" overalls with little blue
shoulder straps for stoles. But even this was not the
worst. For when he picked up the big book and declared with a strong voice, "Lift up your hearts unto
the Lord and hear His Word," he found, to his great
dismay, that he held in his hand, not a Bible, but a
mail-order catalog. And before he could explain these
strange circumstances either to himself or to his congregation, Peter awoke abruptly from his dream, and
found himself pounding nervously on the bed post with
his great round fist. He began to tremble and shake
until it seemed the bed was shaking, too, and he exclaimed into the dark bedroom, "What a night. Oh,

what a night. How can I preach in the daytime if I dream like this all night?"

But so it is sometimes with pulpitpounders, especially when they begin their work in a new congregation.

By the time Peter had polished his black shoes and reviewed his sermon notes, eaten his hearty breakfast, and walked to his church, he felt fit as an apostle and was ready to give the devil a merry chase.

Now in this church it was customary for the pastor to give a little talk to the Sunday school each Sabbath morning. And so the first talk Peter gave was to the children. This pleased the preacher immensely, for he loved to speak in simple language so the little ones could understand. Indeed, he often told his deacons, "I haven't preached a good sermon unless the children can understand it." For you see, Peter knew that if the children understood the sermon, the grownups would too, and then everybody would be blessed.

As soon as the children saw their new friend, the Rev. Dr. P. P. Pulpitpounder, they loved him. Perhaps it was because he was so round and jolly—like Santa Claus. Or perhaps it was because he spoke to them with the kindness of Jesus. Or maybe it was even because of the gleeful twinkle in his eye. For whatever reason it might have been, the children loved their new pastor as soon as their eyes fell upon him, and they never took their eyes off him as long as he spoke.

Peter thought it would be nice to get acquainted with the children and to teach them, right from the start, how he wanted to be addressed. With a big lov-

ing smile that won the hearts of all the boys and girls, he told them, "Pastor Peter Pulpitpounder is such a long name, you children might wear yourselves out just saying it."

All the children laughed and laughed. And then when it got quiet in the room, he continued, "Even Reverend Pulpitpounder is too long to be convenient—and pastors don't care much to be called Reverend anyway." And the children laughed again.

And then he added, "So boys and girls, *Just call me pastor.* You don't even have to use my name—unless you really want to."

When the pastor finished his talk to the children, he sat down on the front bench of the church. The white-haired superintendent rose to his feet and said, "Now I want you boys and girls to remember what you have just been told. We are always to call our minister 'pastor.'" And then turning to Peter Pulpit-pounder the superintendent continued, his face beaming from ear to ear, "Thanks for the good talk, Reverend."

When Peter left the Sunday school assembly, he went to the Bible class and taught his students about the love of Jesus who lived and died for everyone. And when the bell rang, he hurried into his private room beside the chancel to change into his altar robes. By the time he had dressed and had talked to the organist and the choir director about the music arrangements, discussed some problems with the head usher, and even tried to settle a little dispute between two members of the Ladies' Aid, Peter was in first-class condition to conduct the sacred service, especially since this is a task which calls for the greatest quietness of spirit.

All went well for this holy man in the opening service, and when he returned to his private room while the choir sang the anthem, he sat down to catch a breath and breathe a prayer for his sermon.

Now when he was standing by the altar, the pastor had dropped his printed bulletin, so he tried to conduct the rest of the service without it. He took for granted that this congregation would follow the same order of service as was used in the tiny village. So when the choir finished singing, he waited for the next hymn to begin.

Nothing happened for a long, long while, and finally Peter wondered if something had happened to the organist. He put his shining head out of the doorway so he could see her, and across the well-filled church (for churches are always well-filled on a preacher's first

Sunday), the organist whispered loudly, "Announcements, announcements."

Peter was embarrassed by such a blunder, but he walked bravely to his pulpit and made his remarks, telling the people how happy he was to be the new shepherd of the flock. When he went back to his little room, he fanned his blushing face with a parish paper as he thought of the blunder he had made, and sat back in the easy chair to wait for the pulpit hymn to be sung.

Again nothing happened for a long, long time, so Peter put his head through the doorway once more. Again the organist whispered across the church, her hand cupped like a megaphone by her mouth, "Offering, offering."

"Oh dear," thought Peter, "how could a preacher be so foolish as to forget the offering?"

And by the time the pulpit hymn was finally sung and it was time for him to begin his sermon, the pulpit master was so upset by his forgetfulness that he wondered if he might even forget his sermon. But just as he walked up the pulpit steps, he remembered a Bible verse he had asked his confirmands to memorize the day before. It urged:

Trust in the Lord with all your heart,
And do not rely on your own insight.
In all your ways acknowledge him,
And he will make straight [direct] your paths.

As soon as Peter thought of these words, he knew he had nothing to fear, for he had learned long before that the Lord always directs the paths of those who put their trust in Him. Strengthened with these thoughts, Peter Pulpitpounder preached to his new congregation with grace and power, and when his sermon was ended, he vowed he would always repeat these words of trust and confidence whenever he got up to preach—a promise he always kept as long as he served his congregations.

Chapter 5

Now, Where Was I?

WHEN PETER PULPITPOUNDER first came to the big bustling city, he noticed many things were different from the tiny village.

He noticed all the streets were paved, and not just one block of Main Street, and he thought this was ever so lovely, for a car could now drive by his house and hardly any dust would rise; and Peter knew this would make housekeeping easier for Mrs. Pulpitpounder.

And then Peter noticed that the roads in the open country were also paved and he did not have to worry about getting stuck in the mud or sliding in the ditch; and he thought this was mighty fine, too. But even finer, he thought, were the names on all the country roads. When the pastor went calling on his church members who lived outside of town, he could easily find them, for each country road had a name—just like the streets in town.

One thing that startled Peter was the noisy way people traveled about in the city, something which made city life so different from the quiet, sleepy little village. People were hurrying about in street cars that clanged and buses that roared and smelled. They were rushing about in autos so fast that Peter folded his hands and prayed, as he first watched them plunge in

36

front of one another and spin around the corners. He saw the taxicabs rattle over the street car tracks, and he listened to the heavy trains clatter through the subways. He stuffed his fingers in his ears when he heard the airplanes take off from the runway, and he held his hands over his eyes when the jet planes made crazy streaks all over the sky, like a child scribbling with a white crayon on a piece of blue paper.

Another thing which Peter Pulpitpounder noticed about the big city was that almost everyone uptown was dressed in Sunday clothes, even on Monday or Tuesday, to say nothing of the rest of the week. They were even dressed this way on Saturday, and this Peter could not understand at first. In the tiny village, folks wore Sunday clothes on Sunday, and when Monday or Wednesday or Friday came, they wore Monday, Wednesday and Friday clothes, and of course in the tiny village this meant overalls for the men and housedresses for the women. Before long, however, Peter learned that Sunday clothes were the same as Monday clothes for most people in the big city, except that Monday clothes were just Sunday clothes the year before.

At first this wide-eyed clergyman was impressed by the brief cases the businessmen were carrying. "What dignity this lends to the up and coming man" thought Peter. "Some day when I've had a few extra weddings, I must buy myself a brief case, too, so I can look impressive like the other men."

But once, when he was strolling through the park, Peter chanced to see one of these businessmen sit on a bench and lay his brief case on his lap. Wondering just what such dignified men were carrying in those

37

handsome brief cases, Peter ambled by the park bench. How surprised he was, as he glanced out of the corner of his eye, to see the man take a thermos bottle and a ham sandwich from his brief case, together with a banana and a piece of cake. "Well, well," said Peter under his breath, "I can see that I have a few things to learn about the big city. I'm glad I saw this before I wasted my hard-earned wedding money."

But perhaps the thing about the big city church that startled Peter the most was the telephone. Not that he did not have a telephone in his church in the village, for this he most surely did. But in the city church, it sat right on his desk where he could pick it up any time he pleased without going to the wall and talking into a big brown box with a black water spout on the front, a crank on the right side, and what looked like a smooth, black spool on the left. And instead of hearing "central's" voice when he picked up the phone, all he heard was a dial tone; and instead of saying, "I'd like to talk to Pete Olson, please," when he "rang in," all he did was dial a number.

However, it was not because of these things that Peter noticed the phone so much, but rather because it rang all the time. It rang when Peter tried to read, and it rang when Peter tried to pray. It rang when he tried to eat, and it rang when he tried to sleep. It rang when he was talking with people in his office, and it rang when he was out talking with people in their homes. It rang in the morning, and it rang at night, and just so it would not get out of practice, it rang all afternoon, too. It rang in his home, and it rang in his church. In fact, it rang so much that Peter wondered if bells were not ringing in his head.

No sooner would Peter get well into the task at hand until the phone would ring. When the telephone conversation ended, Peter would hang up the receiver, look perplexed and confused, glance over the work he had been doing, and then exclaim, "Now, where was I?" Before he could get well into the task again, the phone would ring once more. And soon his secretary would hear him say again, perhaps absentmindedly, "Now, where was I?," and then he would sigh deeply.

"How different from the tiny village," said Peter to his wife one day as they were driving to the telephone office to pay the monthly bill, discussing the

39

ever-ringing telephone on the way. "Why I could just as well have been born with my left hand attached to my ear, because my arm is in that position most of the time anyway!"

One morning, when the secretary had her day off, Peter was looking for some old records in the darkest closet of the church basement when the telephone rang in the office upstairs. He stood up quickly among the boxes, broom handles, and broken chairs, bumping his bald head on a candelabrum on his way up. The phone rang again.

"I wonder if I can make it," pondered Peter. "Maybe I can if I hurry."

Jumping over a table, Peter landed on an empty scrub bucket, twisting his ankle. The phone rang again. Brushing his irritation aside, the pastor skated through a dozen doorways, skied up the stairway, took a couple of corners on one foot, and glided into the office.

Grabbing the phone, the minister pushed it quickly to his ear and gave out a husky, "Hello."

No answer.

Again Peter gasped, "Hello, hello."

But the caller had already hung up, and Peter was left holding the line like a fisherman. The pastor, being a man of calm and forgiving disposition, laid the phone back on the desk and said quietly, "Blessings on us, one and all."

But after he had sat at his desk for a few minutes to catch his breath, he wondered if something should not be done to train his congregation just when and how to phone a pastor.

"My, my," puffed Peter, as he stuffed his shirt back into his trousers and dusted off his shoes, "a person ought to train for the Olympics, if he plans to be a minister—especially if he expects to survive!"

Chapter 6

The Least of These

ONE LATE AND DARK NIGHT Peter Pulpitpounder was sitting alone in his church office, when the door opened silently in front of him. The shadow of a man fell across the desk, and when the pastor looked up, he saw a big, dark man with a greasy hat and dirty trousers standing in the doorway.

As Peter raised his eyes, the man said in a low, gruff voice, "Hi 'ya, mister."

What little hair the pastor had on the back of his head stood up straight as a donkey's ears, and he felt a cold chill race down his back.

"Yes, sir," ventured Peter slowly. "What can I do for you tonight?"

"Look, mister, I'm not here to make ya' any trouble. I just ran out of gas and grub, and need a little help."

Peter breathed a silent sigh of relief. "Won't you sit down, please?"

"Thanks, mister." As the caller sat down close to the pastor, the odor of whiskey was heavy on his breath. "I'm not askin' for any money, Reverend."

Peter was glad when he heard this, because so many strangers came to his church asking for money to buy food who went straight to the liquor store instead. Since it was late at night, and Peter was going home soon, he decided to let the man come with him so he could fix him a bite to eat. Peter shut the church doors, and when he glanced at the man's car, he thought he had never seen such an old pile of junk in all his life, for its cracked and crooked fenders were tied on with bailing wire, and the spare tire was tied on with a rope.

When the old man had finished the bacon and eggs which Peter fixed for him while the rest of the family was sleeping, he pushed his chair from the table and began to leave.

"Just a moment," the pastor interrupted. "I can't give you much, but there is one thing I have which I can give, and this I want to share with you."

And then, taking his Testament from his pocket, he read to this poor stranger about the good Lord who

44

loves everyone, especially those in need. And he said a short prayer, asking God to watch over this homeless child of His—a lonely child no one else seemed to care about at all.

After a long, thoughtful silence, Peter and his new friend walked quietly out of the house. The stranger followed the pastor's car to the gas station, where Peter bought him some gas, charging the bill until the end of the month, because he, too, had run out of money. As the old man shook Peter's hand, he said, "I want to thank you, Reverend, for what you've done for me."

And then, as he brushed away a tear that was falling down his rough and whiskered cheek, he continued, "When I came to your office, Reverend, I told you a lie. I had planned to rough ya' up, if I needed to, so I could get some money; but now you've made me feel different about life. Thanks a million. I'll never forget you."

Peter drove away with deep joy in his heart. He remembered the words of Jesus, "As you did it to the least of these my brethren, you did it to me." "How fortunate I am to have a home of my own," thought Peter as he drove back to the parsonage. "What a difference it makes to have someone love you and to know someone cares."

And then, as he put the car in the garage, Peter added, "This man almost had me scared tonight. I thought maybe he had a gun, and—probably he did! I was almost as frightened as the night someone broke into our church." And Peter's mind went back to one of the most exciting nights he had ever known.

Chapter 7

A Thief in the Night

PASTOR PULPITPOUNDER turned the key good and tight in the garage door. He was thinking about the night he sat up late in his office typing sermon notes, when he suddenly heard noises in the church. At first he hardly noticed it.

But soon the parson knew this noise was the sound of footsteps in the basement. Uncertain of what he should do, the pastor sat silently at his typewriter, and tried to think about his sermon. It seemed that the footsteps were coming closer to the office door, and so Peter, whose back was to the door as he typed, turned his head and tossed a quick glance toward the doorway. He looked at the door for a moment, and then he looked at his typing, trying all the while to concentrate on his sermon. In a few moments he stole another glance at the doorway, and then he tried to turn his attention back to his Sunday message.

Before long, Peter decided he simply could not think about sermons while listening to those footsteps. He got up from his chair, and tried to slip quietly toward the basement stairs. But Peter was a heavy man, and he could hardly walk silently, and soon the prowler in the basement heard him coming.

As soon as the burglar heard Peter's steps, she ran to the stairway that opened to the alley. It was a Gypsy

woman, and she knew her way around in the church,
even in the dark. She had been in the church many
times before, and had stolen money from the office secretary's desk and from the Sunday school birthday
banks.

Peter ran down the stairs and around the church.
Just as he got to the alley, he saw a black skirt start
up the street into the dark night. It was useless for
him to run any longer, because this woman was too
far in the lead, and Peter was hardly built to run a
foot race. He walked slowly back to his office, wondering what to do. Unable to think about his sermon
any longer, he decided to close the typewriter and go
home, for it was very late, and this time Peter was
shaken.

Now Peter knew who his visitor was because he had seen her once before. Indeed, he had seen her very distinctly. It happened one day when the pastor walked into the sanctuary and found the Gypsy there. He thought nothing of this at first, because he thought she had come in to pray. But when she saw the pastor, she ran quickly down the aisle, looking about her from side to side, like one who is running from danger.

Peter decided to follow this woman, hoping he could find where she lived and talk with her. For several blocks the woman walked slowly, not knowing that she was being shadowed. But then she caught a glimpse of Peter turning the corner she had just turned, and she became alarmed.

When Peter rounded the corner in front of a large church, the woman was no longer anywhere to be seen. Thinking she might have stepped into the church, Peter walked into the front hall. In the silence of this sacred place, he could hear the panting of this woman who had climbed to the balcony and was catching her breath.

Peter didn't make a sound. When the woman came down the stairs, she had to walk past him in the narrow doorway. He looked carefully at this strange woman, but before he could speak a word, she slipped past him and fled.

In a few minutes, the pastor was at the police station. Although he was glad to see people come to the churches at any time, he was suspicious that this person had not come to pray.

A few days later when our good friend, Peter Paul,

was going to Ladies' Aid, he saw the same Gypsy passing the church, a heavy satchel in her arms. Peter walked toward her, for he still hoped to meet her and learn where she lived. He was eager to see if she was in great need. "Perhaps," he thought, "I could even help her, so she would no longer want to steal." And his pastor's heart went out in kindness to this poor, but wretched, person.

But when the Gypsy woman recognized the pastor, she snapped her face in the other direction, and hurried down the street. Peter rushed to his car and drove around the block. When he got to the school yard, he saw the Gypsy resting on the merry-go-round, her bundle on the ground, for she had run around the block.

Peter drove quickly to the police station. "I think I can take you to the woman I told you about," he said to the chief.

In a minute, Peter was riding in the prowl car past the school yard. "I'll let you off at the church," the policeman instructed, "and then I'll pick her up."

When Ladies' Aid was over, Peter excused himself from the coffee hour, and went back to the police station. "It's quite a story, pastor," the chief explained. "Her bag contained a toaster, a waffle iron, two portable radios, and other appliances she had shop lifted. She keeps them in a locker at the bus depot, and then takes them to the pawn shops, one at a time. It's quite a racket."

Peter was sorry that this woman had not let him talk with her. For now she was in trouble with the law for stealing, and even though it was his church that she had also robbed, he held no hatred for this poor soul. He even loved her with the love of Jesus. And although he knew that justice had to be done to this clever thief, the pastor still hoped they would not punish her too severely.

But while a few of the callers at Pastor Pulpit-pounder's church were more like wolves that came to steal than like sheep that came for shepherding, most of them were honest folks who needed the guidance of the Master whom Peter followed, and who came with honest intentions, knowing the pastor would give them his honest interest and concern.

And one time Peter said to his wife, "My initials stand for the three main phases of a minister's work: for he's a preacher, a promoter, and a pastor. And I like the last the best."

"Yes," replied his understanding wife, "I know you love to preach about Jesus, and I know it's important for you to promote many causes in His kingdom. But I think you are the happiest when you do the work of a pastor."

Chapter 8

Shepherding

IT HAD BEEN a long and hard day.

Peter had gone to the church office unusually early to spend the morning working on his pastoral report to the congregation. After lunch he had driven far out to the north end of the city to call at the Veteran's Hospital, and had stopped to give private communion to some of his aged church members on the way back home. Now it was time to have dinner with his family.

Since he was driving by the church, the pastor stopped at the church office to see if the secretary had left any notes on his desk before she went home for the day. As he laid his communion set on the shelf, the telephone rang.

A strange voice inquired, "Is this the Reverend of the church?"

"Yes," replied Peter, "this is Pastor Pulpitpounder."

"Reverend," the voice continued, "I have a terrible problem, and I *must* talk to someone. If I don't, I'm afraid of what I might do to myself. I know you don't know me because I don't attend any church, but . . ."

Peter interrupted, "Would you like to talk with me right now?"

"If I could talk with you right now," replied the strange and broken voice, "you just don't know how

51

much it would mean to me. But it's so late in the day to bother you just now."

"Not at all," returned the minister. "It doesn't matter what time it is. I'll look for you at my office in ten minutes."

When the conversation ended, Peter opened the window for a little fresh air and said to himself, "It's late, and I'm tired; but I wouldn't feel right about going home, if I knew someone in this world was in desperate need of my help."

By the time Peter had called his wife to say he would be late for dinner, the stranger appeared at the office door, and as the conversation continued late into the dinner hour, the two men talked about many things. But they talked most about this stranger's home, and the struggle that he and his wife were having to find happiness together. For they quarreled and fought most of the time, and the tottering home looked as though it might fall to pieces at any moment—like the house built on sand in Jesus' story.

Peter listened closely to everything the stranger said. He loved people, and he always gave them his full attention when they talked with him. Sometimes he simply said to this man, "I see," or sometimes, "I understand." And then sometimes he even said, "I know just how you feel." For Peter was an understanding counselor, and when he listened to people tell about their problems, he never made them feel criticized or condemned, because he knew it was not his place to judge others. This was God's job, and Peter knew it. And Peter remembered that God is also merciful and kind, more ready to forgive than to condemn. He knew Jesus accepted people just as they were, and this Peter wanted to do also.

Down into the deep valley of despair the pastor went with this troubled man, and before the stranger left the office with a heart that was now unburdened, Peter bowed his head and said a simple prayer to the heavenly Father, asking Him to help this couple overcome their problems with the help of Jesus. The stranger shook the pastor's hand firmly, thanking him for what he had done; and as he left the office, he promised to come back in a few days to discuss these problems further.

"Bring your wife, too," invited the pastor, "if she wants to come. I'm sure we can discuss these things together in the spirit of Jesus."

Such a conversation had become almost a daily experience with Peter Pulpitpounder, as he served the big church in the bustling city. He had done much counseling in the tiny village over the years, but there was so much more to be done in the big city, because there were so many more people; and not a few of them had trouble getting along with others, and with themselves.

Peter wanted to be a good shepherd to his flock, and many were the times he helped people who were not members of any flock at all. For the world is full of wounded sheep, sheep that have been bruised by life and its thorny pathways, and Peter had a tender heart that loved to bind up the wounds and soothe the bruises with the gospel's balm of Gilead. For many frightened people were playing "He loves, He loves me not" with the petals of their daily experience, concluding that because so many bad things had happened to them, God did not love them any more.

And then there were those who thought God did not care any longer because He did not seem to hear their prayers. "God doesn't answer my prayers," some people told him, and then Peter had to help them understand that sometimes God has to say No to us when we ask, because we ask foolishly. "It's like the little boy who asks his mother for matches before he's old enough to handle them safely," Peter would say. For sometimes God *is* answering our prayers when we do not think He is paying attention at all. For there are times when He who knows best must answer us in ways that seem so wrong at the time, but which would seem so right, if we only saw the whole picture, and understood as He understands. "So we will love and trust Him deeply, even when we do not understand," Peter would say.

Sometimes people came to this kindly man because they were in trouble with the law, for they had stolen, or lied, or cheated, or even killed; and they could not find their way out of the maze by themselves. And sometimes they came because they drank too much, and drinking had led them into many hard and shameful situations.

Sometimes it was the young people who came with their questions about dating and dancing and dice and a dozen other things, especially such things as what they should do with their lives when they grew up. Peter had a listening ear and a kind word for everyone that came. He loved to do this part of his work as much as anything he did, because then he felt he was being a real shepherd to his people.

Of course, Dr. Pulpitpounder could not always help the people who came to him, for sometimes they seemed to put themselves right in their own way; and Peter wished these people would stop resisting the Holy Spirit, and let themselves be helped. Peter had long before learned he must "spin carefully, spin prayerfully, but leave the thread to God," as a great man said one time.

Sometimes this counselor helped folks far more than he thought he did just because he loved them so much, for love does more to heal and help than anything else that God has made. And Peter knew that he was sure to help people at least a little, if he only got them to trust God more, and then *just live,* one day at a time.

Sometimes Peter felt his biggest task was to help people withstand the trials of the moment in Christian faith, even though the hardship could not be fully explained, as when the young couple lost their only child in its first year of life, plucked like a tiny flower in the bud, fallen like ripe fruit too early to the ground. Peter helped these sad people see that God does not always give us an explanation of our hardships, but that He gives something far better: the help and comfort of His holy presence, which is so much better than an explanation. They learned that sometimes we must live a little longer before we can understand some things, and that some things must wait for the brighter light of heaven before they can be understood. For sometimes, from the light of heaven, our whole life on earth can be seen as *just a little while,* and so many things can be endured, if it is for just a little while.

And so, on and on, day after day, year after year, Peter Pulpitpounder counseled with young and old alike, helping them to walk up the rugged hills and down into the dark valleys. He was indeed a pastor above all else. And Peter loved the work of shepherding with all his heart.

And one day as he straightened the calendar on his desk, he said to himself, "I guess the reason I like to be called 'Pastor' is that this word means 'shepherd,' and above all else, I want to be a good shepherd to my sheep."

And then he added, laying his glasses on the desk blotter, "Of course, I'm only the undershepherd. The real Shepherd is the Lord."

Chapter 9

Christmas Eve

FEW DAYS WERE filled with more excitement and
festivity in the Pulpitpounder household than the day
before Christmas. The house was decorated from stem
to stern with bells and wreaths, mistletoe and candles,

and above all else, the children's Christmas tree. Not that the tree was decorated elegantly, because the children did the decorating; but it was done with enthusiasm and zeal, and few Christmas trees were ever more beautiful in the eyes of children than this one with its dazzling lights, its sparkling tinsel, its piles of presents spread under the branches, and topping it all, its Star of Bethlehem which touched the ceiling and pointed heavenward to the loving Father who sent His only Son to be the manger Child.

When Peter came home early on this joyous day, he was met by his children who ran to the door and hugged his legs and pulled his hands, shouting, "Oh daddy, we can hardly wait!" After he had given each of his Christmas angels a tender kiss, he noticed a special Yuletide smell in the living room, for the house was filled with the odor of evergreen and burning candles. But the aroma that was strongest was the smell of lutfisk[1] cooking in the kitchen, and Peter exclaimed, "Now I know it's Christmas Eve, because it smells of lutfisk in our house."

The smell of lutfisk, which to some people is the worst smell that God ever created, is the best smell in all the world to one who loves it; for it is the perfect proof that Christmas Eve has come, and Peter told his wife that it just couldn't seem like Christmas Eve in his house, if the smell of lutfisk cooking on the stove wasn't there.

And so to the kitchen stove went Peter, lifting the lid on each saucepan to inspect its contents. Under one lid he found the "potatiskorv,"[2] steaming in its "baloney" skins, and the pastor's mouth began to water as he thought of the tasty meal his family was about to enjoy.

Under another lid he found the brown beans cooking, and he exclaimed with youthful excitement, "What is Christmas Eve without 'bruna bönor'³?"

Next to the white sauce (for the lutfisk), Peter discovered the boiled potatoes; and glancing to the kitchen counter, he saw the loaves of homemade rye bread that just belonged to Christmas Eve, and a pound of real butter, something they had only at Christmas and Easter.

By the bread, Peter found the jars of root beer which Mrs. Pulpitpounder had put up weeks before, and as he watched the bubbles sparkle to the top, he just knew that this year's "dricka"[4] was going to be the best ever.

Although Peter was warned not to open the oven, he stole a little peek through the steaming glass on the oven door, and there, to his great delight, he saw the "ostkaka"[5] turning a golden brown—just right for the topping of lingenberries.

"What a night for a happy home," thought Peter. "Surely this is the life I love, and that I want my childen to love."

After Peter carried in the kindling and the logs, he built a crackling fire in the Christmas-stockinged fireplace; and by the time the fire had burned to a glowing light, it was time for the family to eat their Christmas Eve "kalas."[6] The lamps were turned out, and the candles were lighted, including the red candles on the table, which was covered with the white linen cloth used only at Christmas and when there was company. The room was quiet and peaceful, like the Judean hills where the shepherds watched their sleeping sheep, and the warmth of the fire made everyone glow inside with the spirit of Christmas.

Bowing their heads at the festive table, the nine Pulpitpounders folded their hands reverently and said,

> "Come, Lord Jesus, be our guest,
> And let these gifts to us be blest. Amen."

And they thought of the greatest gift in all the world, the gift of the blessed Lord Jesus, whom Mary wrapped in swaddling clothes and laid in the manger, because there was no room for them in the inn.

And as the excited family devoured the rich food and talked and laughed, Peter thought in his heart, "This is the way a home should be. I love each one of my manger babes, and also their mother who gave them to me."

When dinner was done, and the candles were burning low, Carol Marie went into her father's study and brought him the family Bible. Peter turned to the second chapter of Luke and read aloud:

In those days a decree went out from Caesar Augustus that all the world should be enrolled. This was the first enrollment, when Quirinius was governor of Syria. And all went to be enrolled, each to his own city. And Joseph also went up from Galilee, from the city of Nazareth, to Judea, to the city of David, which is called Bethlehem, because he was of the house and lineage of David, to be enrolled with Mary, his betrothed, who was with child. And while they were there, the time came for her to be delivered. And she gave birth to her first-born son and wrapped him in swaddling clothes, and laid him in a manger, because there was no place for them in the inn.

And in that region there were shepherds out in the field, keeping watch over their flock by night. And an angel of the Lord appeared to them, and the glory of the Lord shone around them, and they were filled with fear. And the angel said to them, "Be not afraid; for behold, I bring you good news of a great joy which will come to all the people; for to you is born this day in the city of David a Savior, who is Christ the Lord. And this will be a sign for you: you will find a babe wrapped in swaddling clothes and lying in a manger." And suddenly there was with the angel a multitude of the heavenly host praising God and saying,

> "Glory to God in the highest,
> and on earth peace among men with whom
>   he is pleased!"

When the angels went away from them into heaven, the shepherds said to one another, "Let us go over to Bethlehem and see this thing that has happened, which the Lord has made known to us." And they went with haste, and found Mary and Joseph, and the babe lying in a manger. And when they saw it they made known the saying which had been told them concerning this child; and all who heard it wondered at what the shepherds told them. But Mary kept all these things, pondering them in her heart. And the shepherds returned, glorifying and praising God for all they had heard and seen, as it had been told them.

The children loved to hear this story of Jesus' birth, and when Peter had said a Christmas prayer, and each of the children had added his little petitions, the family began to sing some Christmas carols. Helen Margaret wanted them to sing "Silent Night," and Matthew asked them to sing "Hark, the Herald Angels Sing." And with so many in the family, it was not hard to make it sound like an angel choir, especially with Peter singing a clear, ringing tenor, Luke a manly bass, and the little children carrying the melody with their delightful bell-like voices. For now, after many years,

Peter and his wife had the family chorus they dreamed of having when they were engaged to be married.

The family would have kept singing longer, for everyone was singing from the bottom of his heart and the top of his voice, but more excitement was to come, and soon the children were clearing the table and doing the dishes while Peter put another log on the fire. Little Nancy Elizabeth was too tiny to be trusted with the delicate Christmas dishes, especially the thin glasses used only when the family had "dricka," so Peter let her open one of her presents while she waited, and she jumped up and down in her excitement when she saw the little toy dog and shouted, "Just what I wanted for Christmas!"

Now Peter needed little help in making himself look like Santa Claus with his round, round tummy and his twinkling eyes; and, of course, his loud, jolly voice was first-class equipment as he came noisily into the room, laughing and calling the children with a boisterous, "Ho, ho, ho. Come and see what Santa has for little children."

Around the sparkling Christmas tree the family sat, and before Santa would let them open a single present, he had them sing, "Gather Around the Christmas Tree." A box was placed by the tree for the wrapping paper and the ribbons, and as each person was handed a present from Santa, the whole family watched him unwrap it, and put the paper into the box. What excitement and what dancing spirits these children had as they tore open their presents, and with wide-open eyes saw for the first time the new doll, the fire truck, the game box, the handkerchiefs and stockings, and the

63

neckties! Each person put his precious treasures in a little pile, and when all the gifts were opened, Peter took a picture of his beaming family.

As soon as the flash bulb popped, Mrs. Pulpit-pounder instructed her little ones, "Now, children, put your presents under the tree and then we must hurry off to bed. It's getting late for children who have to be up by five o'clock and go to Julotta!"[7]

It seemed that they had surely just fallen off to sleep when the alarm clock called the family to get up, and as soon as the children were awakened by Peter's "Merry Christmas, darling," each little pajama-clad lad and lassie tripped into the living room to steal another glance at his new presents. Peter had turned on the tree lights before he called his children, because he knew they would hurry to the tree as soon as their sleepy minds could realize it was Christmas morning.

In their new stockings and shirts, neckties and dresses which they had just received the night before, it was indeed a handsome family that sat down to eat the big oranges and dippy eggs which they always had before Julotta. Peter did not have time for "påtår,"[8] because he had to hurry his family into the car and drive them through the darkness of the big city to the church.

When they got to church, quiet Christmas music was coming from the tower, and as the Pulpitpounder family walked into the candlelighted sanctuary, the strains of "All Hail to Thee, O Blessed Morn" were filling the quiet, crisp morning air.

And when the service, with its special choirs and its holy stillness, its thrilling message, and its treasured hymns was ended, the people walked out of the big church into the big city, and discovered that it had turned light while the service was finishing; for the candles had burned low in the windows and the first blush of early dawn could be seen peeking softly through the stained glass. As Peter shook hands with his congregation, wishing each one "Merry Christmas," he thought to himself, "This is the thrill of the Julotta service: that we come in when it's dark and go out when it's light, for darkness never speaks the last word."

When the Pulpitpounders got home from church, they had their "real" breakfast, and by the time it was noon, it seemed that a whole day had already passed. And while the children played with their toys in the afternoon, and some of them napped, Mrs. Pulpitpounder told her husband, "Christmas always seems two days long to me, and the morning always seems like the afternoon."

Chapter 10

The Pulpit Master

PETER WAS a man of many sides. And each time another side of this colorful man was turned to the light, he sparkled like a diamond turning in the sun.

There was that side in Peter's nature that loved people, and when he was with them he simply sparkled and beamed. But there was also that side of this delightful man that yearned to be alone at times, for this busy minister had little time to keep company just with himself; and he felt sometimes that he needed to come apart from the crowd, and be alone with his soul and its Maker to let the wells of the spirit fill up again.

Another side of this reverend man was turned to suffering and need, for he had a chord in the inner harp of his being that always played rich and deep tones when he saw folks who were sorrowing, or suffering, or in serious need of any kind.

And then there was that side of Peter Pulpit-pounder's stature that was turned to beauty in all its forms. Sometimes it was the beauty in nature that captured his eyes, and sometimes it was the beauty in music that captured his ears. Indeed, never was Peter brought to tears quite so quickly as when he listened to stirring music that spoke to his inner being. Mrs. Pulpitpounder noticed that her husband would weep

more readily when he heard rich music than when he heard sad tidings.

Still another side in this pastor's life was that which was seen from the pulpit. Pastor Pulpitpounder loved to preach about Jesus, and the radiant expression that shone on his face as he told of the life that is life indeed gave as much inspiration to his listeners as the words that he spoke. Sometimes, in fact, when Peter had little time to prepare his sermon, he still gave his people such a feeling of joy in being Christians that they left the church strengthened by the light of his countenance, if not greatly blessed by the weight of his words. Many times Peter told his congregation that their calling in life was to be radiant Christians in whatever occupation happened to be theirs, and Peter, himself, was the shining example.

Yes, Peter Pulpitpounder loved to preach. And strange as it may seem, Peter even loved to preach at funerals. One would hardly have guessed that such a joyous man would actually *like* to preach at such somber occasions, hardly, that is, until one remembers that this is the place where Christian radiance is needed most. And this is the time—what with hearts heavy, and hopes shattered, and faith sometimes shaken—that pastors can bring the comfort of the gospel in such a living way that people will listen with ears that are open and hearts that are ready to be blessed.

Peter loved to preach at funerals, not because he liked to deal with sad things, but because he knew he was giving comfort to the sad, strength to the weak, and to the frightened a reason not to be afraid. For sometimes when he preached at his regular services, Peter wondered how deep his messages were going through the head to the heart, for there is that about a sermon which is like a hypodermic needle: to do any good it must get under the skin. But when Peter preached at a funeral, he could see that everyone was drinking in his words, and with his words they drank the Word which is the water of life and the only fountain that can cool the burning heart.

Sometimes people came to his funerals who otherwise never came to church, and Peter felt that here the Master had a chance to knock at some shadowed door that had been locked tight for many a year. And one time Peter said in a funeral message, "Don't wait for tomorrow to open your door to Jesus; tonight may even be too late."

Of course, it was not easy for this pulpit master to

speak to his people at funerals, for he, too, felt grief in losing a friend; and every time he laid someone to rest, Peter felt that *he* had lost something precious, too. But Peter remembered that he had not really lost these Christian friends who put their faith in Jesus, for they were simply going on ahead, like pioneers, to a land that is much better than this, and to a place where time means nothing to anyone, for there it is transformed into eternity.

Little wonder, then, that Peter loved to preach at funerals, for the message that Jesus died that we might not die forever is never so real as when dear ones lay their dead away. And to Peter the funeral of a Christian was not a time of morbid hopelessness, but a holy celebration when folks had a chance to re-echo the Scripture, "By grace you have been saved through faith; and this is not your own doing, it is the gift of God—not because of works, lest any man should boast."

Perhaps the most joyous feeling that ever went through the souls of Peter and his people was sensed by the congregation one day at the funeral of an aged Christian who had died on Easter Day. The funeral was held in the church. No weeping in uncontrollable waves was heard. Instead, the rafters of the sanctuary rang with the triumphant message of the risen Lord, who gave His life on the cross and walked away from the empty tomb a victor over death and a conqueror of the grave.

Everyone knew how this seasoned disciple of Jesus had lived in the power of his conquering King and had died in the vibrant faith of the saints of God.

They knew he had left this land of crosses to dwell forever in a land of crowns. This was no farewell forever; it was a homecoming in heaven!

And as the son of this blessed saint walked out of church that day, he said to Peter Pulpitpounder, "Pastor, I have never felt more triumphant and joyous in all my life." "Yes," said Peter, "the story of Easter makes a Christian's funeral the gathering of warriors for the shout of victory."

And as Peter went home from the cemetery that day after committing this friend of earth to the care of heaven, he turned still another side of his nature to the light, and once more the diamond sparkled in the sun as he said, "Someday, somewhere, another pastor will lay my body away for the long rest. I hope *my* children will also have the faith to say, 'This is our father's day of victory. We've never felt more joyous and triumphant!'"

Chapter 11

Vacation Time

FOR SEVERAL MONTHS Peter Pulpitpounder had served the big church in the bustling city. He had learned the names of all his members and was getting the feel of the polished parish with its combination of the dignified and the dainty, the wealthy and the desti- tute, the imposing and the unassuming.

Peter was also learning to let his secretary keep the records and run the office, something he appreciated deeply because this pastor, like so many others, had been accustomed to doing all these little details him- self, and now he was glad to dismiss these things from his mind, so he could turn his energies to things which only a pastor can do.

One morning, when the children had left the break- fast table and the personable parson was finishing his second cup of coffee, he confided to his ever-helpful wife, "I believe one of the best gifts a pastor can be given is a good secretary."

"Yes, Peter," replied Mrs. Pulpitpounder, "I don't know what you would do without her help. She *is* a gift from heaven."

And then, as the pastor's wife put the coffee pot back on the stove, she looked up suddenly when an unexpected thought popped into her head. "Peter," she exclaimed, "do you realize that conference time will be here before we know it?"

"It doesn't seem possible!" said Peter. "But I haven't forgotten. I've had it in my appointment book for several months. In fact, the other day one of my deacons told me he was glad conference was coming soon, because he felt I needed a good rest." And then Peter laughed heartily at this foolish remark.

But Mrs. Pulpitpounder did not laugh. She only said flatly, "Well, you get mighty little rest at a convention, if you want my opinion. I don't envy you sitting for hours on those hard church benches, listening to reports day after day."

"I wouldn't mind the reports," Peter replied, "if it weren't for the resolutions. But then we can always slip out for coffee when they begin to quibble over the split infinitives."

"Careful dear," warned Peter

"But did you hear what Mrs. Olson said the other day?" Mrs. Pulpitpounder's voice was beginning to rise. "She had the nerve to . . ."

"Careful, dear," warned Peter with his hand held aloft—like a benediction. "We don't gossip about our church members."

Mrs. Pulpitpounder put a stack of plates in the dish water and lowered her voice. "Well, anyway, you should know she thinks convention week should be a part of your vacation, and . . ."

"Not really," Peter retorted, as he wiped his mouth with a napkin and began to rise. "Why, she should go to a convention just once and she'd soon . . ."

"Careful, Peter," warned Mrs. Pulpitpounder, "we don't gossip about our church people, remember?"

Hardly before he knew it, conference time was upon him, and one evening during the convention, Peter Pulpitpounder attended his seminary class reunion. It was years since his graduating class was ordained, and at the reunion Peter noticed with surprise how much his classmates had changed. Not only were most of them thinner on the top; they were also thicker around the middle. And because life does many things to people as they struggle with it, all the pastors looked much older than Peter had remembered. And late that night, after the old songs had been sung and the pranks of the good old school days were recalled, Peter went back to his hotel feeling a little sad and nostalgic. He thought of his classmates and how much they had changed, and he said to himself, as he looked into the mirror, "It's strange I haven't changed like the other men."

". . . strange I haven't changed . . ."

When Dr. Pulpitpounder returned from the convention, and had rested sufficiently, he was soon back in the swing of a heavy schedule. He commended his secretary for the fine way things were kept moving in his absence, and soon Peter was surrounded with the clicking of typewriters, the ringing of telephones, and the clanking of mimeographs and addressing machines.

And then one day, the Pulpitpounder car was heavily loaded, and all the children took their reserved seats in the family Ford. The time for an honest-to-goodness vacation had arrived, and the Pulpitpounder auto started up the hills to the camping grounds and the fishing stream. They had planned to spend their vacation visiting Peter's wife's mother, but since she had written that she had a fever, and thought it best for them not to come, they decided on a camping trip in the mountains.

As the parsonage family was putting up the tent, with all the children pounding stakes and pulling ropes like one big team, Peter said to his family, "This is what I call a real vacation! We can get away from the tensions of our busy living and rest—and fish. I can feel the trout on my line already!"

And then he continued, "The best part of the vacation for me is the chance to be with my wife and children. I have so little time for my family when we're at home."

"Yes," replied Mrs. Pulpitpounder, "with all the children in our family, it's hard to give each one the time you'd like. But here you can. The only problem is that with all these people sleeping in the tent tonight, this will seem like just another convention to you."

But Peter did not mind the crowded tent, and early the next morning, he had forgotten all the little wor-

ries and the big concerns that are wrapped up in the life of a busy parish, and was out on the stream casting his line and pulling in the rainbow and the brook trout with the best of them.

But one morning, Mrs. Pulpitpounder heard a little whelp come from Pepper, their black Heinz 57 puppy dog. Quickly she sat up in her sleeping bag and shook her husband. "Peter, Peter. I think Pepper is having her puppies."

In a moment Peter was in his overalls and out of the tent, peering into the hollow tree stump that Pepper had chosen for her camp site. Stealing quietly back to the tent, he whispered, "Mother, come quickly."

Pepper was just beginning to have her pups, and when the day was half gone, she was the proud puppy mother of seven little squirming infants who were squealing and crawling about, newer than tomorrow's issue of the daily paper.

But Pepper could hardly have been more proud than Pastor Pulpitpounder, and as he helped his wife straighten up a nursery for the little pups, he said, "It's just right ·for a pastor's dog to have seven pups, because in the Bible seven is a holy number. Shall we name them after the seven days of creation or shall we use the seven petitions of the Lord's Prayer?"

"I'm not worrying about the names," Mrs. Pulpitpounder replied. "But I do remember that in the Bible seven also stands for completion. I hope this means Pepper isn't having any more puppies, especially when we're on vacation."

77

Chapter 12

Preacher's Boy

IF THERE WAS one time when Peter Pulpitpounder was unhappy, it was when he heard someone say the preacher's boys were different from the other boys in town.

To be sure, the Pulpitpounder boys did their share of mischief and made their quota of noise, but this didn't make them different from the others; it made them like all the rest.

Now, if it could be said that they did *more* of the mischief or made *more* of the noise than the other boys in town, then Peter would have been happy to admit his sons were different. But Peter was a fair and honest man, and he knew this was not the case.

Nor were Peter's boys different because of being more angelic than the rest, for although Mrs. Pulpitpounder might have wished for her sons to be flawless examples to the other boys in the Sunday school, such was hardly the situation; and the Sunday school teachers had to work just as hard to squelch the bad, and bring out the best, in the preacher's boys as they did from any other lads in their classes.

But there were exceptions.

If Luke, when he was a younger lad, had been the apple of his mother's eye and the pride of his father's heart, there was still Paul who, even in his few years, had gained a reputation for quite the opposite. Not that Paul was really bad; he was simply full of energy that nothing could ever exhaust. For if life is made up mainly of matter and energy in some sort of reasonable ratio, here was a specimen of God's creation that had defied the ratio; for this lad seemed to be all energy and mighty little matter. And after he had outrun the energies of his mother and father, his teachers and cub sponsors, and even his brothers and sisters, Paul still had boundless energy left to burn, and he burned still more looking for challenging places and ideas with which to burn the rest.

Paul loved to talk, and his talking was the trial of every teacher he had, with his incessant whispering in the classroom and his loud jabbering on the playground. In fact, Paul hardly knew what it was to leave school with the other children, because his talking earned him a silent hour with the teacher after school almost every day, and every day when he came home late, Paul and his mother chanted the same ritual:

"Why are you late?" was the standard question.

"I talked," was the regular reply.

One of Paul's favorite habitations was the sycamore tree in the back yard of the parsonage. No one in the neighborhood could scramble up into a tree as fast as Paul, and no one dared to swing from the branches with the abandon and fearless ease of this little acrobatic monkey. Sometimes he would pretend his tree house was a pulpit and Paul, who inherited the sparkling eyes and beaming radiance of his father's countenance, would shout to the high heavens around him and the barns and alleys beneath him that they must change their wretched ways, or the great and fearful day would most surely come upon them.

Now, Mrs. Pulpitpounder took a somewhat dimmer view of the ideas and activities of her energetic son. She thought it most fortunate that the Creator had given him such an agile body, for without it he would have broken into a thousand pieces long before. But she wasn't sure the Creator had agreed to watch over this little bundle of enthusiasm if he insisted on jumping and swinging in the branches in the way the Lord intended only for the lower species of His great creation.

Sometimes, therefore, it became necessary for Mrs. Pulpitpounder to exercise *her* imagination and enthusiasm in the swinging of limbs and the pounding of branches. And let it never be said that such a capable woman as the mother of these seven children was ever lacking in imagination, to say nothing of enthusiasm. And, so, since her husband was seldom at home in the day time, there were moments when the sycamore branches became useful to her for things other than swinging from or climbing in.

One day as the pastor and his lovely wife were enjoying a quiet hour of afternoon coffee in the shade of their own back yard, they heard the familiar rustling of leaves in the branches above them. Almost spilling his coffee, Peter jumped to his feet and exploded, "I do declare, we never should have given that boy a second name—or at least it shouldn't have been Zacchaeus."

"I don't know if the name has anything to do with it," Mrs. Pulpitpounder said, "but we must do some-

thing firm and convincing to keep that boy from breaking his neck."

And then, looking up into the sycamore tree, she called sternly to her son, "Young man, you come down from that tree this very minute or we'll have a little session in the woodshed."

The storm in her eyes and the threat in her voice were all Paul needed to be convinced, and before anyone heard another sound, the little preacher was down from the tree and on the ground, on the alley side of the back fence.

And yet Paul was not a bad child. He was just the one in Peter's quartet of boys who had the most daring and the greatest originality. And Peter told his wife, "You wait and see. Some day the Lord will take all these troublesome traits of Paul's and send them down some useful channel, and then our son will be a leader in the community."

Little did Peter know just how prophetic were his words. For when Paul was out of grammar school and well along in the terrible teens, he began to show signs of unusual leadership, and was even called upon from time to time to give a class speech or enter an oratorical contest.

And when Paul was a senior in high school, he turned his energies to creative things, like writing music, and stories, and even poetry. Of course, the writing was not planned for text books on American literature, but it had the same vibrant and energetic feeling that ran through everything that Paul Zacchaeus Pulpitpounder did from playing football to singing in the choir. And one day the teacher gave him an "A" for a poem he turned in as a class assignment. He called it "Compensation."

> The fellas used to josh me,
>   And the girls used to, too.
> They'd say, "I guess there'll never be
>   A fella just like you.
> You've got an awful gift of gab.
>   You talk a steady stream:
> On playground, hall, and science lab
>   You're never off the beam.

An' playmates weren't the only ones
  Who told me of my fault,
For Mom and Dad would man the guns
  Agin' me till I'd halt!
An' teachers, too. They were the worst!
  They never gave me peace,
Cause, course, I always started first
  An' never seemed to cease.

But now I don't quite understand
  Why everything should change.
The folks don't motion with their hand
  For me to stop—it's strange.
They tell me, "Son, you should be proud
  We've reared you up so well;
Not everyone can meet the crowd
  And freely talk a spell."

Chapter 13

Wedding Bells

"BUT, FATHER," insisted Luke as he sat across the desk from Peter Pulpitpounder, "we don't want to wait until I graduate from medical school to get married."

"It's true, Pastor," added Lydia, who was a loyal member of Peter's church. "Luke and I have been engaged for almost a year, and we think it would be a great advantage for us to be married while Luke takes his internship and finishes school."

Peter was puzzled. Somehow the idea of his first child being old enough for marriage seemed unreal, if not impossible. He wanted his son to be happy, and he never doubted for a moment that Lydia was the girl he should marry. But he felt they should wait until Luke had finished medical school and was ready to take his special language training to be a medical missionary.

"Don't you think it would be wiser to wait until you're in language school?" suggested Peter.

"You didn't wait until you were out of school to get married, Dad," Luke reminded him.

Peter could see he was making little headway with his opinion. He realized that in the end, it would be the couple themselves who would decide; and before the pastoral visit was over, Peter had entered a very special date in his little black appointment book.

Several sessions of pre-marital counseling followed, and much excitement was seen in the parsonage and in Lydia's home. And when all the preparations were made, and the showers had been given, the time arrived for the vesper hour wedding.

Peter and Paul, the twins, were chosen as candlelighters, and as they went about the church with burning tapers, an air of festivity filled the sanctuary.

When the solos were sung by Lydia's brother, the organist began the processional march. Peter walked reverently to the altar and said a silent prayer, imploring God's blessing upon the new home now to be established. When he turned to the congregation, which had filled the sanctuary to overflowing, the first bridesmaid started up the center aisle.

Peter smiled. It was all so beautiful in the candle-lighted church, and as the bride's attendants continued to come to the chancel in their lovely gowns, joined by the groom's attendants dressed in white coats and black trousers, Peter thought, "What a lovely way to be married! I do hope their home will be as beautiful as their wedding."

And then as the bride came up the aisle holding her father's arm, the congregation arose and the proud father gave his daughter away. A little tear came to the eyes of Lydia's mother as she remembered, "I gave Lydia to her father such a short time ago, and now he is giving her to her husband."

When the wedding party had assembled at the altar with Lydia holding Luke's arm as she stood before her minister in all her happy beauty, Peter began to read:

"In the Name of the Father, and of the Son, and of the Holy Spirit. Dearly beloved."[1]

How much these words meant to Peter as he read them this time!

"Marriage is a holy estate instituted of God Himself for the preservation of the human family, for the mutual help of those who enter into this sacred bond, to lighten the burdens of life, to alleviate its unavoidable cares, and by careful nurture to provide for the happiness of posterity. This is a holy institution; its obligations and objects are likewise holy."

---

[1] The quotations are from the Augustana Lutheran marriage ceremony.

And then, turning to his son, he said,

"It is the duty of the husband to love and honor his wife."

Luke had been taught from childhood that love was the most important ingredient in life. He knew what real love was and had discovered that it was more than a man's attraction to a woman's physical beauty. He had not found it hard to love such an attractive woman as Lydia, but the wedding ceremony said it was his *duty* to love her. He remembered his church's teachings about the sacred duty of love, and promised himself before the altar of God he would remember that his love for Lydia was not only an exciting emotion to be felt in the moonlight, but also the most sacred duty of the home, the bond that holds couples firmly together when hard times or tempting circumstances could so easily pull them apart.

Then, turning to the lovely bride, Peter continued,

"It is the duty of the wife to love her husband, share with him tenderly and faithfully the cares of the household, and at all times so conduct herself as to be his true helpmeet."

Mrs. Pulpitpounder put a little lace handkerchief to her eyes as she thought of the many cares of the household she and Peter had shared over the twenty-five years of their happy marriage, for this night which Luke and Lydia had chosen as their wedding day was also *their* twenty-fifth wedding anniversary. She had been a loving helpmate to Peter all these years, and she thanked the God who created marriage for the experiences, both hard and happy, which they had shared together.

And then, after Pastor Pulpitpounder had turned to the altar with the wedding rings to ask God's blessing upon the solemn covenant of love and marriage which these rings symbolized, Luke and Lydia took their wedding vows, looking into the eyes of the one they loved. And when the pastor declared them man and wife, Lydia smiled and tenderly pressed the hand of her husband with whom she had promised to share her life in the mission fields across the sea.

When Peter told the newlyweds that the Bible teaches us "the two shall become one flesh," he thought of the wonderful oneness that he and his wife had known these many years. It was as if they were indeed but one person, each one simply the other half of the same being, and each one feeling himself incomplete without the complementing nature of the other. He reminded them that in the sight of God, their marriage was to be for life, recalling the words of Jesus, "What therefore God hath joined together, let not man put asunder."

Peter wondered if these young people could grasp the full meaning of his statement, "Receive with patience and thanksgiving all that may betide you in the providence of God." Little did anyone know what might be in store for this new family in God's providence, but Peter was sure their Christian training had prepared Luke and Lydia to receive whatever might betide them with patience and thanksgiving, just as they had seen these virtues practiced by their parents.

88

What a hallowed moment it was when Peter knelt with the bride and groom before God's presence and in the quietness of the candlelighted church, the pastor offered a special prayer for this new home. He asked God to hear their prayers, and be their very present help when they called upon Him, and prayed that when their pilgrimage was ended, the Father above would take them both to His heavenly home where they could be together forever.

And then, facing the devoted couple who were still kneeling in the stillness of that holy hour, the pastor said,

"God Almighty send His light and truth to keep you all the days of your life. The hand of God protect you. His holy angels accompany you. God the Father, and the Son, and the Holy Spirit cause His grace to be mighty upon you. Amen."

Together they prayed the Lord's Prayer and when Peter pronounced God's benediction upon this Christian home, a lump came into his throat, and he paused to swallow before he could finish,

"The Lord lift up His countenance upon you and give you peace. In the name of the Father, and of the Son, and of the Holy Spirit. Amen."

And when Luke and Lydia embraced one another in the wedding kiss, Peter and his wife were as one person in their tender feelings. Mrs. Pulpitpounder sat with her six children in the front bench of the church and tried to smile, and Peter stood at the altar by his

oldest son, and smiled through tears that ran un-
ashamed down the cheeks of this man who was both
happy and sad and could not tell which feeling was
the stronger. Luke was now beginning where Peter
had begun twenty-five years before, and the pastor's
mind was filled with memories. He looked across the
church to his dearly beloved wife and wondered if they
would still be living when Luke and Lydia celebrated
their twenty-fifth wedding anniversary.

And as the wedding party hurried happily down the
aisle and the guests left the sanctuary for the reception
hall, Peter and his wife stood together in the empty
church and said, "Whatever may betide us in the provi-

dence of God, we know that through faith in Jesus, we will all be together in the Father's house of many mansions."

And Peter took his bride into his arms where Luke and Lydia had just stood and—they both smiled!